D1362069

There is a tree

Written and Illustrated
by
Marti Richtmyer Nash

There is a tree

Story and pictures by Marti Richtmyer Nash

For information address:
Blue Barn Books
139 North Prospect Street
Burlington, Vermont 05401

Design Eugenie S. Delaney
Print production by Kaye Alexander

First Edition 1000 copies
ISBN 978-0-615-13939-5
Library of Congress control number: 2007902345

Printed in China.

for

Madeline Jane

There is a tree in the woods,

And high up on one of its branches is me.

I sit there — quiet as a mouse — watching

what passes by above,

below,

and all around.

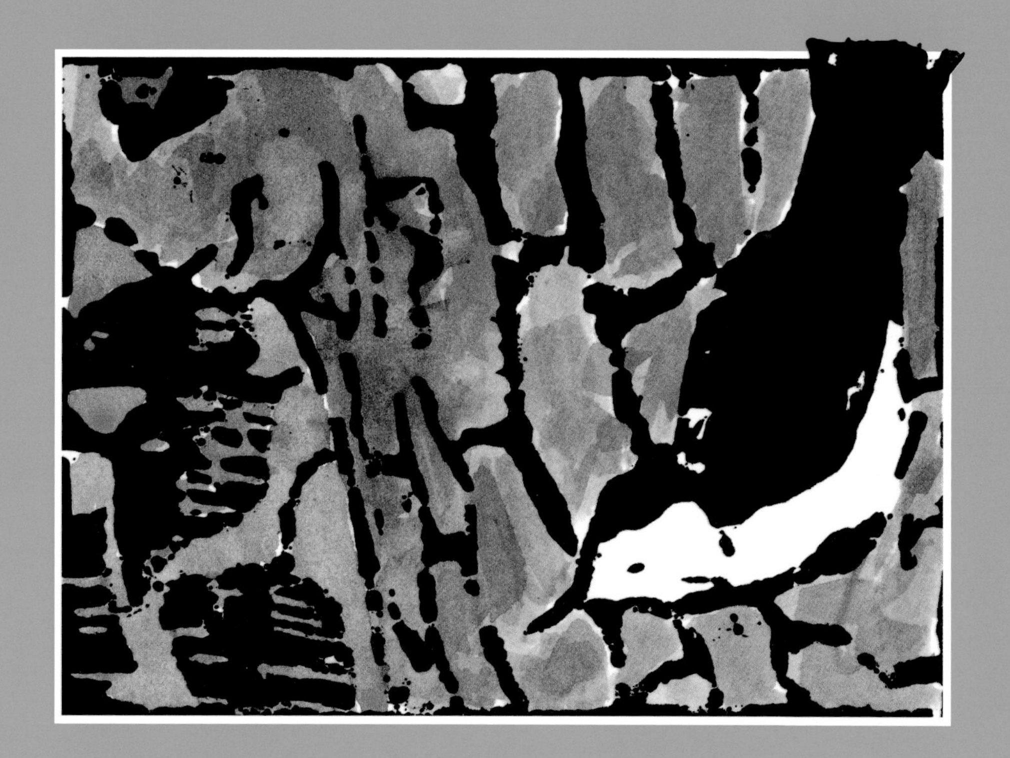

I see a nuthatch picking at the bark of a tree. Is it searching for insects?

I see a deer stop to nibble the

new leaves. It comes, and then goes,

without a sound.

I see a red squirrel flick its bushy tail.

"Churr! Churr!" it scolds.

Am I in its favorite tree?

I see a robin fly through the

branches right past my nose. I feel the

breeze its wings make.

I see a rabbit hop, hop, hop through the tall grass. Between hops it sniffs the air, and listens.

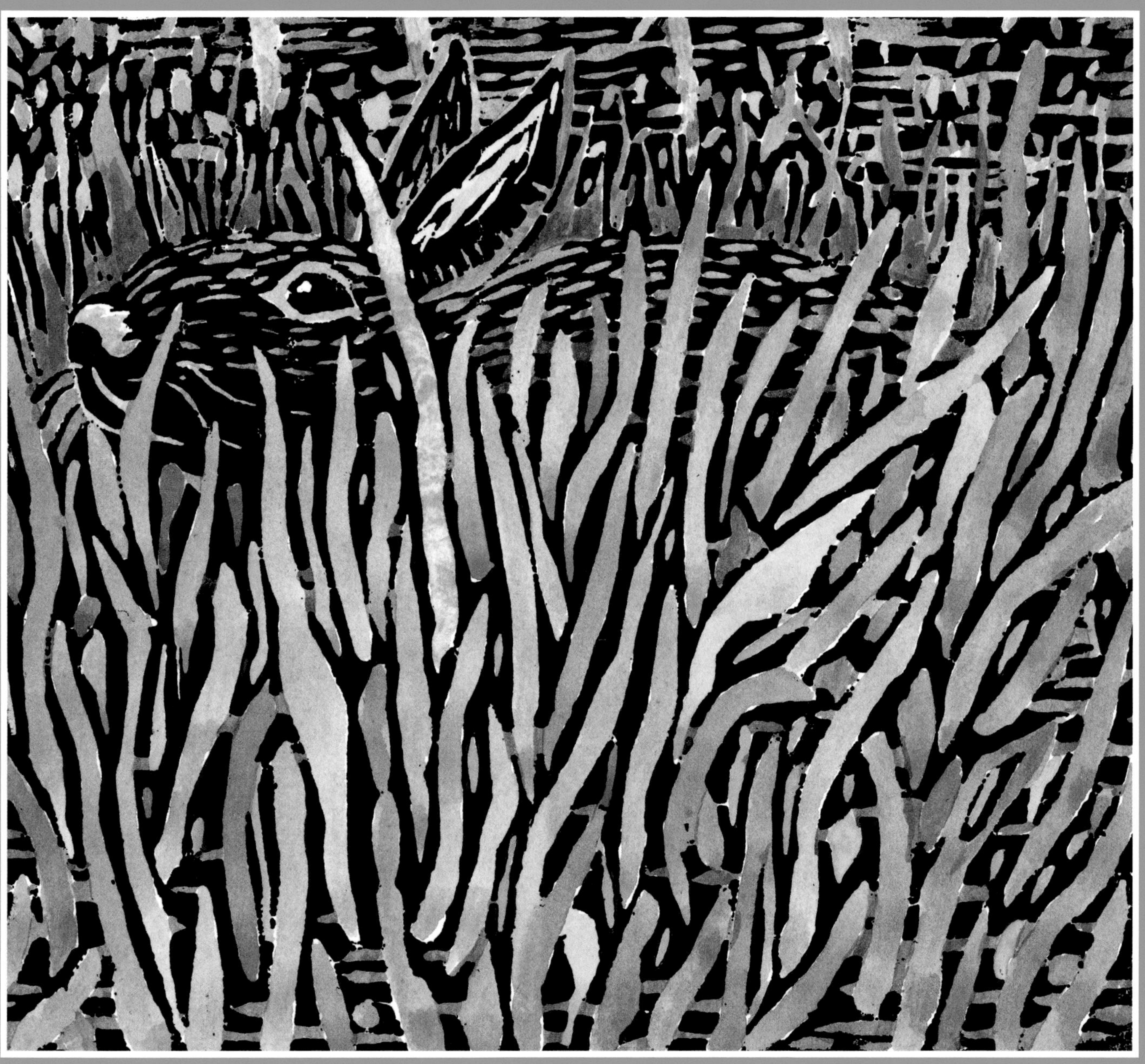

I see a red fox move silently

along the trail. What is it following?

I am glad it is not my tree!

I see a beaver gnaw on a willow tree.

I see a butterfly come to rest on a leaf. It folds its wings like closing a book.

I see a striped skunk waddle by in no hurry. Who would chase a skunk, anyway?

I see the clouds turn

from white to colors of the setting sun.

Soon the moon and stars will light

the night sky.

Will you tell me

what YOU see?

The End